Dancing Masks of Africa

Dancing Masks of Africa

by
CHRISTINE PRICE

CHARLES SCRIBNER'S SONS
NEW YORK

For my neighbors
Christopher
Loran
Stephen
Gregory
and Nicholas

The masks are coming,

the dancing masks—

Listen to the music of their dance!

Listen to their coming

with the fluting and the drumming and the song;

with the thunder of drums,

and the rattle of drums,

and the <u>don-don</u> ringing of the gong,

and the dancing of the hammers on the wooden keys,

the ripple-water music running up and down—

the music of the <u>balafon</u>!

The masks are coming,
the dancing masks,
with faces
    of animals,
faces of men,

and faces of spirits

with staring eyes,

masks that leap high
          from the sun-dry earth,
and masks that whirl in the dust.

In secret places
the masks have waited,
hidden away in the sacred woods.
They wait in the dark for the festival day,
waiting for the dancers to put them on,
waiting in stillness for the time to come,
the time to rise up and dance.

The people are ready when the great day dawns,

ready for the coming of the masks.

You can hear the drums

in the middle of the village,

and see how the earth is built up in a mound,

smooth and round like a man's bald head,

there in the village dancing place.

And the old men sit

in the dancing place,

waiting for the masks to come.

The old men sit, but the women run,

running with the drumming to the edge of the wood,

to call to the first of the masks to come—

the Powerful One, Protector of Animals,

Terrible Lord of the Beasts of the Bush!

Three times they run

and three times they call,

chanting their call to him,

chanting again,

and then—

HE COMES!

His mask is a leopard that leaps on its prey.
With the leap of a leopard he springs on the mound!

Towering in majesty over the people,
Oloko has come from the heart of the forest,
the leopard warrior, young and strong.

He stands there in glory,
and then he is gone!

The Lord of the Beasts
has gone back to the forest,
swift as a leopard
that leaps on its prey.
And out of the shadows,
the dark green coolness,
comes the mask of the Healer, the Bringer of Rain,
moving with gentleness, prudent and wise,
the Curer of Sickness, the Healer of Pain.

And now the people go leaping and singing
to welcome the noblest of all the masks.
See him come gliding out of the forest,
his mighty headdress veiled in white.
With the steps of a king
he circles the village,
shedding his blessing on every house.

And when his veil is cast away,

they see at last the kingly mask

of royal Orangun, who spreads his blessing,

making his people calm and cool,

calm and cool

as a rain-filled pool

in a hot and thirsty land.

The masks have danced,

this festival day,

for the good of all the people.

The masks dance, the African masks,

for village people and people of towns,

for farmers and fishermen,

hunters and kings,

so that life for all may be rich and strong,

and men at peace together.

When the antelope masks come out to dance,

their steps are a prayer for the seeds to grow.

They dance like the Great One of long ago,

the Antelope-spirit

who taught the people

to dig the earth

and sow the grain,

and tend its growing in sun and rain.

They dance for the farmers, to urge them on

to work for a joyful harvest time,

a season when earth will give its best,

and stores of grain will overflow

with food for everyone.

After the harvest is gathered in,

and the year is near its end,

watch for the masks that come by night,

kindly spirits that carry a blessing—

safety from danger,

safety from sickness,

joy for the children

and peace for the old.

And laughter they bring

as they dance and sing

until the dawn of day,

mocking the lazy,

the angry,

the proud,

the gossiping women and quarrelsome men

and children who disobey!

And here is the mask that seeks out witches

and punishes troublemakers;

and the great black mask
that glides and slides,
with jingling bells
and cowrie shells,

and takes his seat at the forest's edge,
to judge the people and speak the law.

And children learn what the masks can teach,
at the time of their growing up.

Then, deep in the bush,
in the secret places,
the girls will learn
what their mothers know—
how to be beautiful
and strong,
and wise in the wisdom
of women and wives,
the wisdom from
long ago.

And the boys will see,

in the secret places,

the masks that as men

they must learn to wear,

masks that can make them

more than men—

spirits of power

and hunters of witches,

fighters of evil

and breakers of spells.

Chasers of witches and haters of witchcraft,

here they come striding, the giant masks,

feet in the dust and heads in the sky!

Stiff-legged prancers,
bell-ringing dancers,
swaying and swinging
and sitting on air!
When they are weary,
they rest on the rooftops!
All of the people
go running to see them,
and only the witches
are trembling with fear.

And here are the masks that <u>please</u> the witches,

to make them turn from their wicked ways.

The masks come dancing, two by two,

leg-rattles clashing in time with the drums.

Bright dresses they wear,

and they bear on their heads

cars and snakes and sewing machines,

hunters, policemen, and kings and queens,

all of them dancing, twisting and twirling,

nimble and quick to the beat of the drums,

till the wicked witches, the plotters of evil,

are so busy watching

the dance of the masks,

they forget their magic, forget their power,

and all are at peace together.

The masks dance,
the African masks,
for the good of all the people.

When someone has died, the masks will come—
masks of heroes, long dead, returning,
whirling and swirling
like flames in the wind,
spirits of ancestors,
spirits of kings.

When someone has died, the masks will come,
masks of spirits of forest and stream,
and people will gather from far away
to honor the dead one in dance.

Out by the red-earth dancing place

they are tuning the xylophone,

with the beating of hammers on wooden keys

and the music running like rippling streams,

as they wait for the masks to come.

The masks are ready in the ju̱ju̱ house,

the windows covered with branches of palm

so no one can see inside.

And the old men who sat with their drinking horns

have gone to join the dance.

And now they are coming,

the jujus are coming,

with the fluting and the drumming and the song.

First come the people

with swords and spears,

and the masks follow after,

feathered like birds,

with the heads of animals,

leopard and cow,

or the faces of men that stare at the sky.

And look how the smallest of them all

is the leader of the dance!

He leaps to the middle of the dancing place,

and the people fall back to give him room.

He lunges and spins

in front of the masks,

to the beating of the drum and the xylophone,

and the rhythm of the rattles on the dancers' legs,

with a stamp,

      stamp,

        STAMP!

Faster and faster

he leads the dance

till he hurls his spear to the hard-stamped earth—
the bright blade stabbing the damp red earth—
and the masks of the spirits of forest and stream
go dancing away to their secret places,
to wait again for the festival day,
the time of living, the time of dying,
the time to come out and dance.

The masks dance,

the African masks,

for the good of all the people.

They dance for the living,

they dance for the dead,

they dance for the babies still unborn

and the children growing up.

They dance for the earth to give its fruit,

and the sky to give its rain,

for days of plenty and nights of rest,

and the curing of sickness and pain.

They dance in the forest,

the village,

the city,

and under the open sky,

and the dust of the dance is a golden cloud,

and the earth is a drum for the dancers' feet,

as they dance so that life may be strong and good

and men may live at peace.

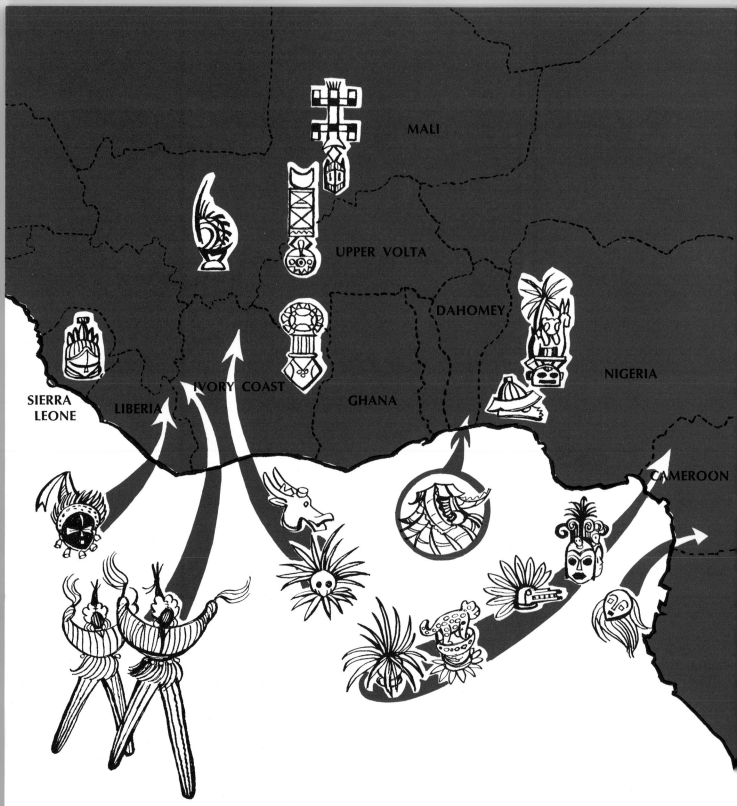

WEST AFRICA

Showing the countries of the MASKS

NOTES ON THE MASKS

The masks in this book—all of them from countries of West Africa—are only a few of the many kinds of masks made by African peoples.

Most masks of Africa belong to secret societies, and only members of those societies are allowed to wear them. Masked dancers are nearly always men, although they may play the part of women in the dance.

The *Gelede* mask, facing the title page, represents a woman, a food-seller in the market. This is a mask of the Yoruba people of Nigeria, and it is worn by a man of the *Gelede* society. These masks are made in matching pairs. The rest of the masks we have seen are listed below:

 Mask of the Senufo people, Ivory Coast. The drum and *balafon* (xylophone) on the preceding pages are played by Senufo musicians in their plumed hats.

Mask of the Bobo people, Upper Volta.

 Mask of the Bangwa people, Cameroon. This Royal Society mask, worn only by men of royal blood, appears at the funeral of a chief.

 *Kanaga* mask of the Dogon people, Mali. These masks dance at funerals and belong to the *Awa*, the Society of Masks.

 Forest-spirit mask of the Pygmies, Cameroon.

Epa mask of the Yoruba people, Nigeria. The great masks of Oloko, the Doctor, and Orangun dance at a festival in some Yoruba villages after the yam harvest.

Chi Wara masks of the Bambara people, Mali. These dance in pairs in springtime. The male mask leads the female, with the young one on her back.

Bedu masks, Ivory Coast. These too dance in pairs, the male mask following the taller female to protect her.

Basinjom mask of the Banyang people, Cameroon.

Gaa-Wree-Wre mask of the Dan people, Liberia.

Bundu mask of the Mende people, Sierra Leone. This type of mask is worn by women who are leaders of *Sande*, the women's society. They are teachers of young girls.

Poro society mask of the Senufo people, Ivory Coast.

Stilt dancers of the Dan people, Ivory Coast.

Gelede mask of the Yoruba people, Nigeria.

Egungun mask of the Yoruba people, Dahomey. These masks also appear in Nigeria.

Mambang masks, Bamenda, Cameroon. These and other masks are often called *jujus* by people in western Cameroon.

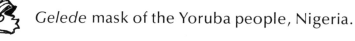